Don't Let the Pigeon Finish This Mini Activity Book!

words by mo willems and mr. warburton

pictures by mo willems

HYPERION BOOKS FOR CHILDREN / New York

An Imprint of Disney Book Group

Hi! I'm the Bus Driver. Welcome to this mini activity book! Look for me at the bottom of each page, and I will tell you what you need for each activity!

Hi! I'm the Duckling! Are you ready to do some really fun activities?

Here I am!

PERFORATED!

Hey there, grown-ups! I'm here to tell you about this mini activity book!

THINGS YOU SHOULD KNOW:

- A book can be read AND played. This book provides loads of opportunities for your kid to do both, alone or with you!

- This book is packed with activities both small and big. Some take up just a page, while others are multi-paged events!

- There is a narrative to this book, but if you want to skip around, go for it!

- Sure, we made these activities to be fun, but we took the extra step of having them all vetted by an early learning specialist. The activities cover a range of abilities, so be ready to help your child with some of the harder ones. Lucky you!

- Every page is perforated, so when your child is done, you can tear out his or her masterpiece and hang it up!

- You'll find a solutions key at the end of the book!

- We use icons throughout the book in the band at the bottom of the page. Here's what they mean:

 Use a pencil (or crayon) for activities that require you to draw or write!

 You'll need a box of crayons for the drawing and coloring pages!

 Have some tape handy!

 Some activities ask you to cut things out — you'll need a pair of scissors. Make sure to help your child with the trickier shapes.

 You might want extra pieces of paper for these activities.

 A few activities require these special items: a stapler and coins (or buttons or paper clips)—please keep a close eye on your kids when they're using these small objects.

**Well, that's about it. Let's get started!
And whatever you do:
don't let the Pigeon finish this mini activity book!**

This book is dedicated to our kids, and yours.

Words: **Mo Willems and Mr. Warburton**

Illustrations: **Mo Willems**

Book design and additional illustrations: **Scott Sosebee**

This special edition was printed for Kohl's Department Stores, Inc. (for distribution on behalf of Kohl's Cares, LLC, its wholly owned subsidiary), by Hyperion Books for Children, an imprint of Disney Book Group, New York.

Kohl's
Style Number 978-1-368-00974-4
Factory Number 211019
2/17–4/17

First Edition, June 2017 | ISBN 978-1-368-00974-4

Printed in Malaysia | Library of Congress Cataloging-in-Publication Data on file.

Visit **hyperionbooksforchildren.com** and **pigeonpresents.com**

Can we please get back to ME?

YOUR NAME

You will need something to write with for this activity!

YAY! Let's draw me!

1.
Start with a big letter "O".
(It appears in words like "Mo"!)

2.
Now, draw a smaller letter "O" inside of it.
(You've drawn a doughnut!)

3.
Next, you have a choice between two letters — "M" or "W" — but draw the letter on its side.
(You made a beak!)

4.
We're going to place the eye next, which is the most important part of the drawing, because the eye shows how the character is feeling. Make sure to darken it in.
(You always look at the darkest part of a drawing first!)

5.
Draw two lines going straight down for the neck.

6.
Next, draw two lines across the neck for the collar.

7.
The body is a circ-angle, a triangle and a circle combined.
(It kind of looks like an ice cream cone that's fallen over.)

Turn the page for more instructions!

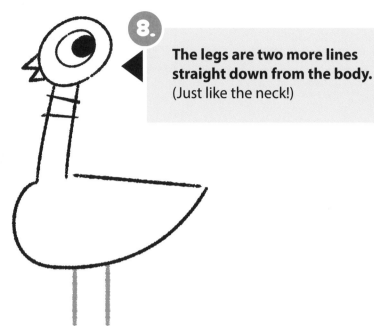

8.

The legs are two more lines straight down from the body.
(Just like the neck!)

9.

Almost done! Draw the letter "V" three times. The first two are upside down for the feet. The third is on its side in the body for the wing.

FINISHED!

Great job! That's an awesome Pigeon!
Once you've gotten the basic drawing down, mix it up. Move his beak, his wings, his eye, and his legs to create lots of different poses and emotions!

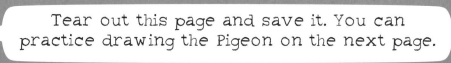

Tear out this page and save it. You can practice drawing the Pigeon on the next page.

HEAD

NECK

BODY

LEGS

Trace the Pigeon on the left, then practice drawing the Pigeon on your own in the space provided.

13

Use these two pages to practice drawing the Pigeon.

HEAD

NECK

BODY

LEGS

If you want to practice even more, get some paper and start drawing!

But first, we have to make a BUS STOP.

And that means . . .

Color this page!

17

IT'S TIME FOR A
BIG ACTIVITY!

1 Pull the **next two pages** out of your mini activity book!

2 Lay them out on a table or on the floor. Make sure the white sides are facing UP!

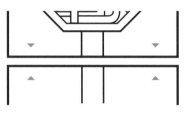

3 Fit the pages together where the arrows indicate.

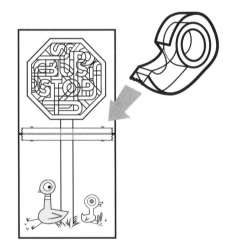

4 Tape the pages together!

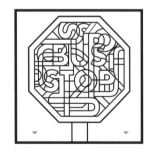

5 Color in all of the shapes with blue dots to read the sign.

6 Hang up your sign on a wall and sit down next to it!

A "BIG ACTIVITY" is one for which you may need a grown-up to help. You'll need these things to do this activity.

TOSS-A-MA-BOB!

3 Points!

Anything that lands
OUTSIDE the circle
is worth 1 point!

The Pigeon sure looks happy! Draw something that makes you happy on one of these pages, then color them both!

 The bus door won't open until it's colored in! Once you finish, turn the page!

HELP! I'm being chased—

What are the Pigeon and Mad Cow running through? A field of grass? Mud? Coleslaw? You decide, and then draw it!

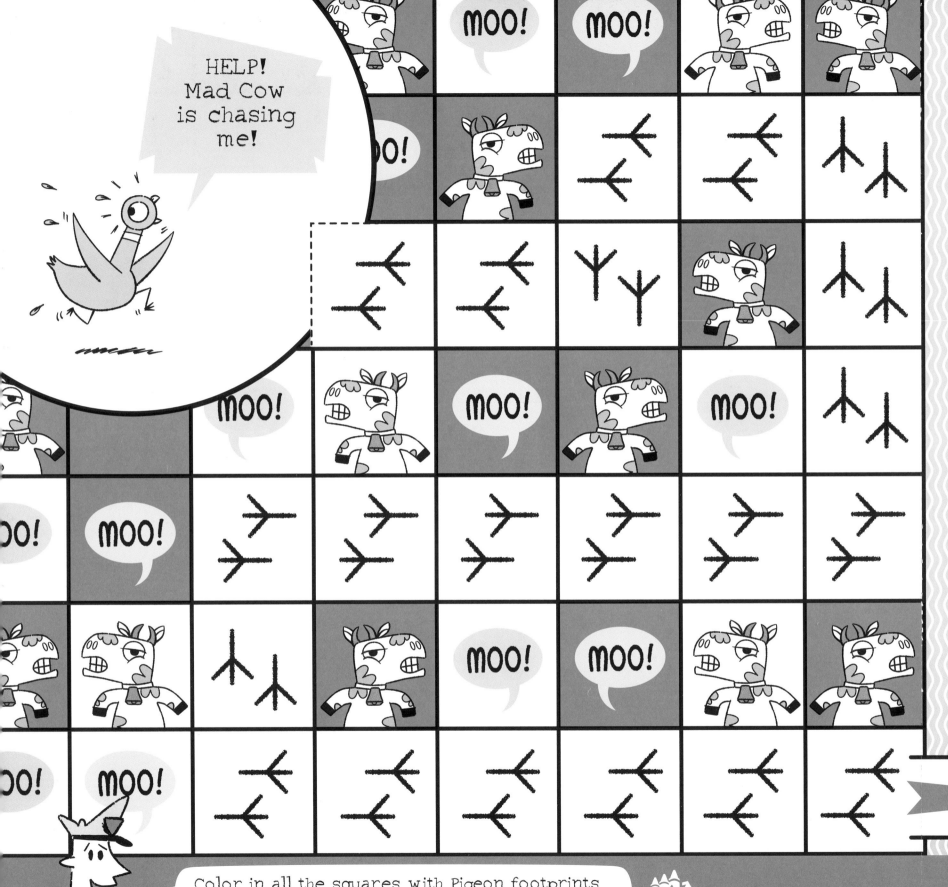

Color in all the squares with Pigeon footprints (人人) to help him escape the Mad Cow!

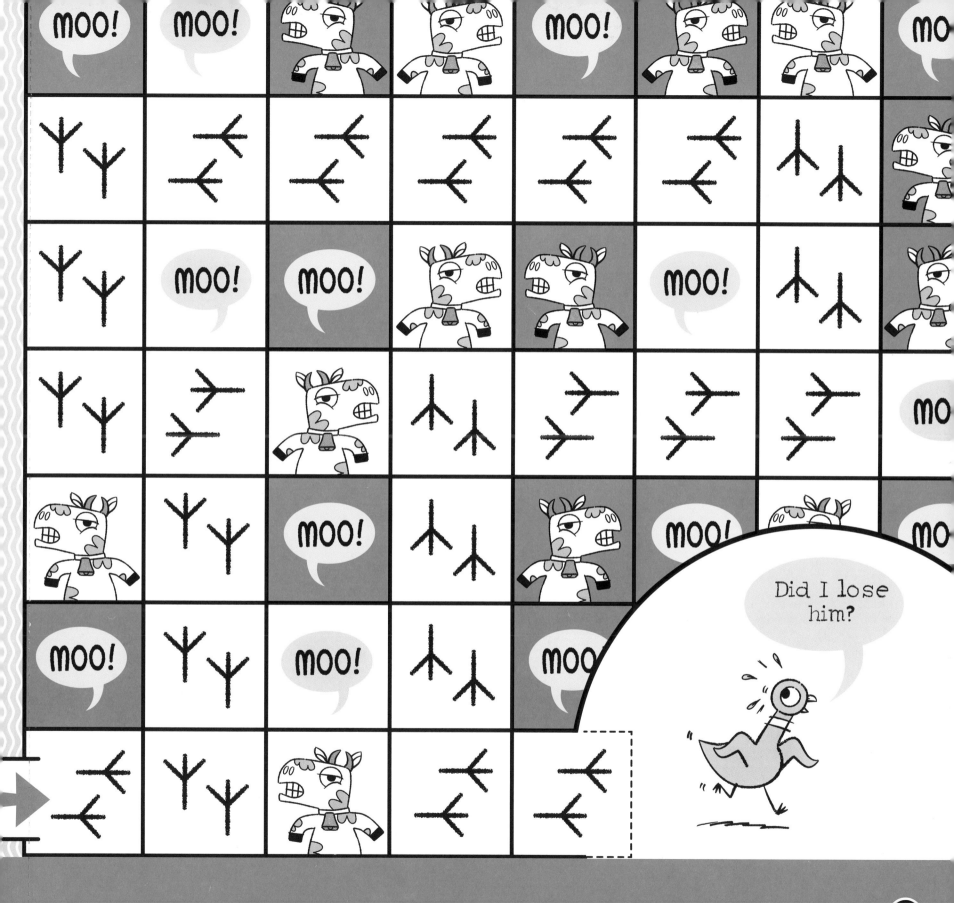

What should we do while the Pigeon is busy playing with the Mad Cow?

The Duckling's idea sounds exciting. Draw as many exclamation points around her head as you can!

Let's play
Toss-a-Ma-Bob!

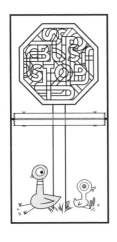

1 Take your bus stop off the wall.

2 Turn it over to magically reveal a Toss-a-Ma-Bob target!

3 Get three coins. (You can also use buttons.)

4 Place your Toss-a-Ma-Bob target on the ground.

5 Step away from the target. Not too close, but not too far.

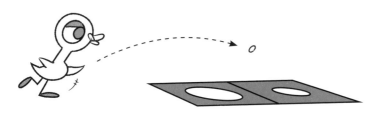

6 Toss a coin at the target. If your coin lands completely within one of the circles, yell "Toss-a-Ma-Bob!"

7 Take turns tossing coins. The first person to reach 10 points is the winner!

To play the game, you'll need some coins or other small objects to toss!

There are lots of fun ways to play Toss-a-Ma-Bob!

If you're right-handed, try throwing the coins with your left hand; or with your right hand if you're a lefty!

Try playing with your eyes closed!

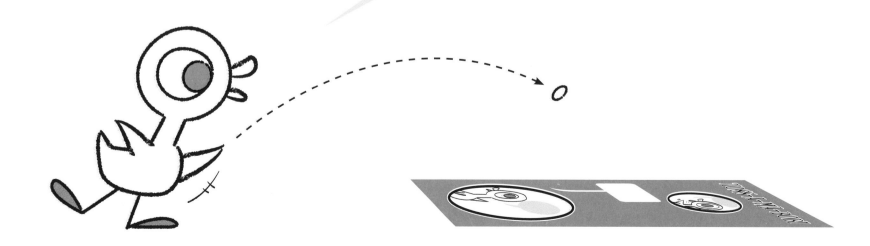

Color this page!

A playdate with the Pigeon! I wonder what his house looks like!

Draw what you think the Pigeon's house looks like!

Okay! Let's follow the path to the Pigeon's house right now!

Start Here

To follow the path, color in all the squares with the Pigeon.

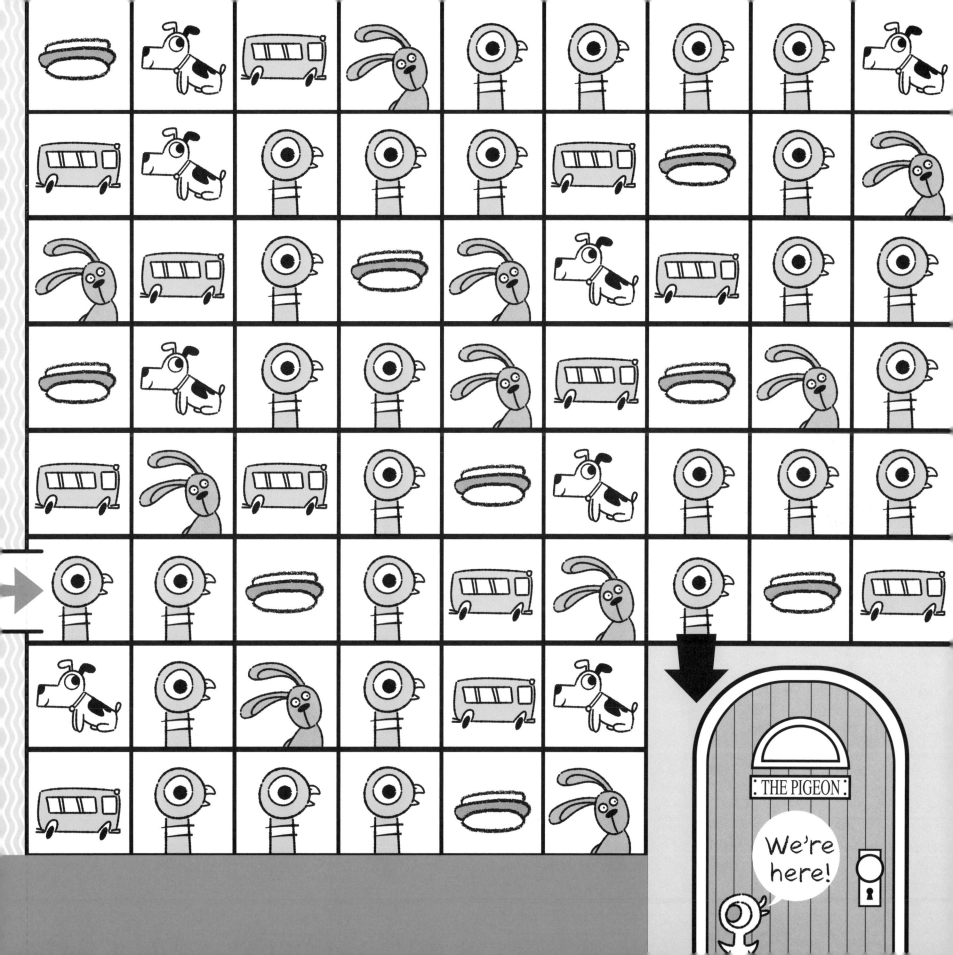

Let's make a knocker to put on the Pigeon's door!

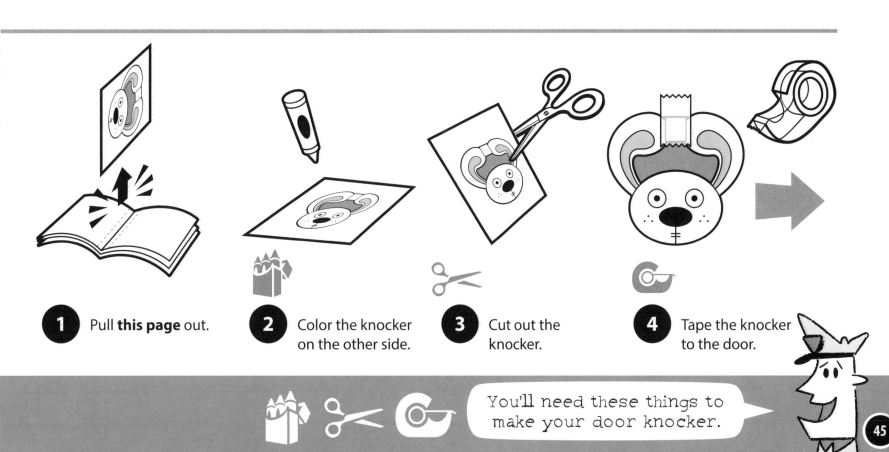

1 Pull **this page** out.

2 Color the knocker on the other side.

3 Cut out the knocker.

4 Tape the knocker to the door.

You'll need these things to make your door knocker.

Hey . . .
that door knocker
looks familiar!

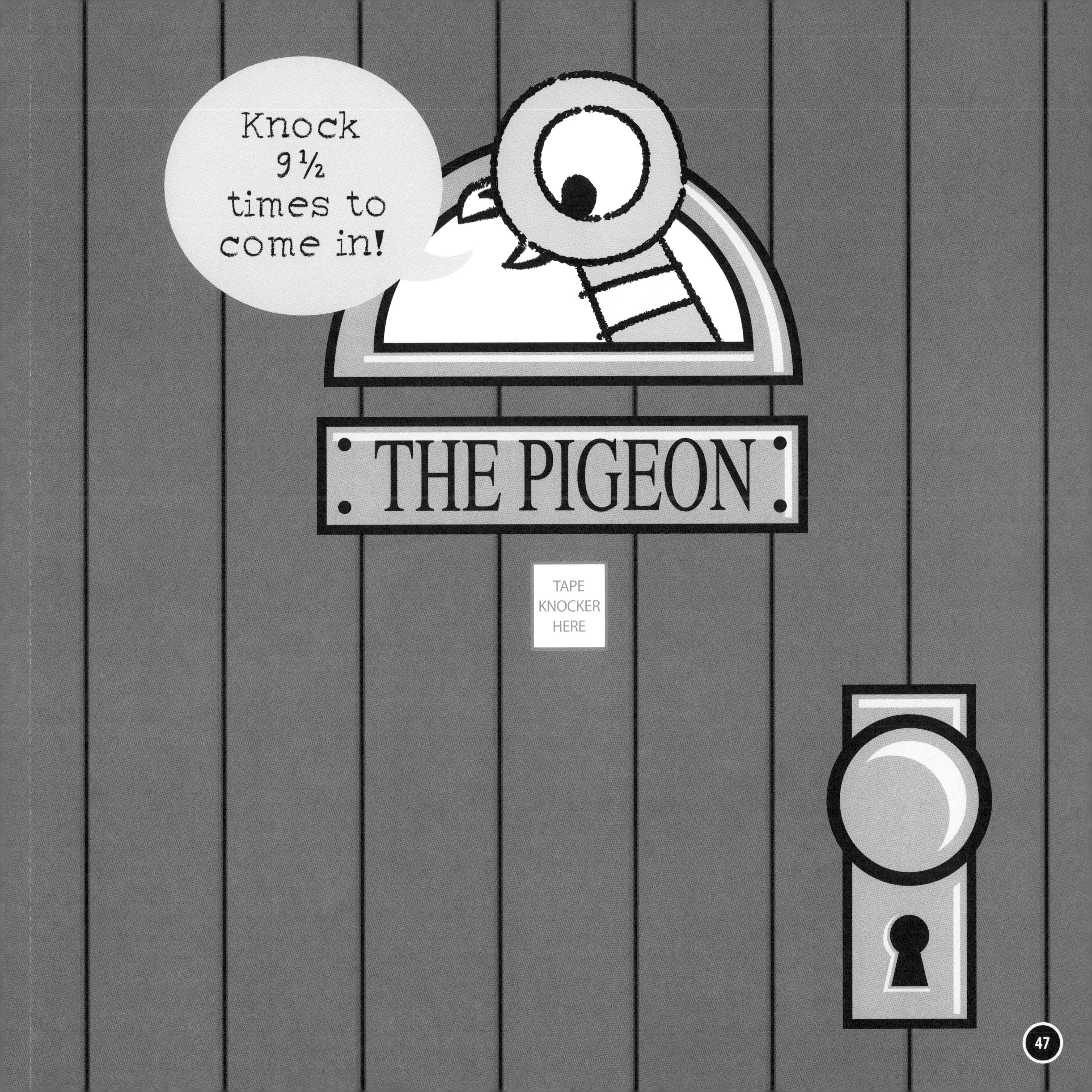
Knock 9½ times to come in!
THE PIGEON
TAPE KNOCKER HERE

48

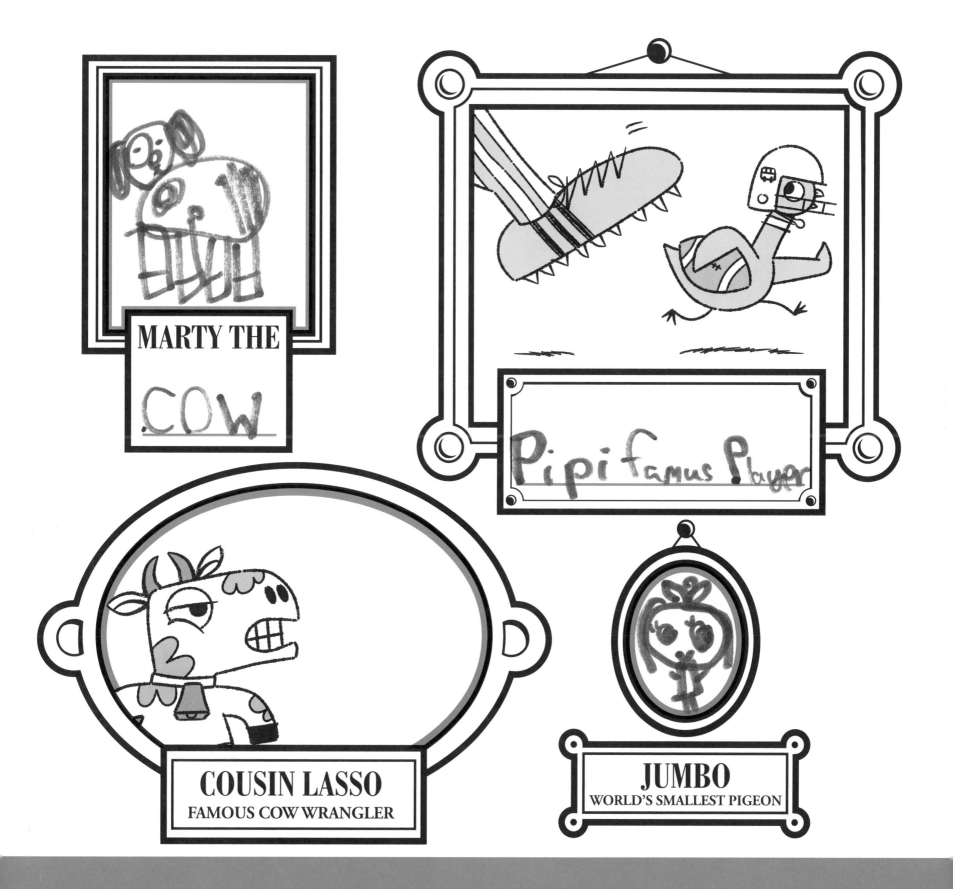

MARTY THE
COW

Pipi famus Player

COUSIN LASSO
FAMOUS COW WRANGLER

JUMBO
WORLD'S SMALLEST PIGEON

SIR PIGEON, THE BLUE KNIGHT

PAPA PIGEON'S FAVORITE HAT

Ma Pigi
Lady

More pictures and names are missing. Fill them in!

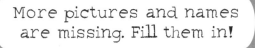

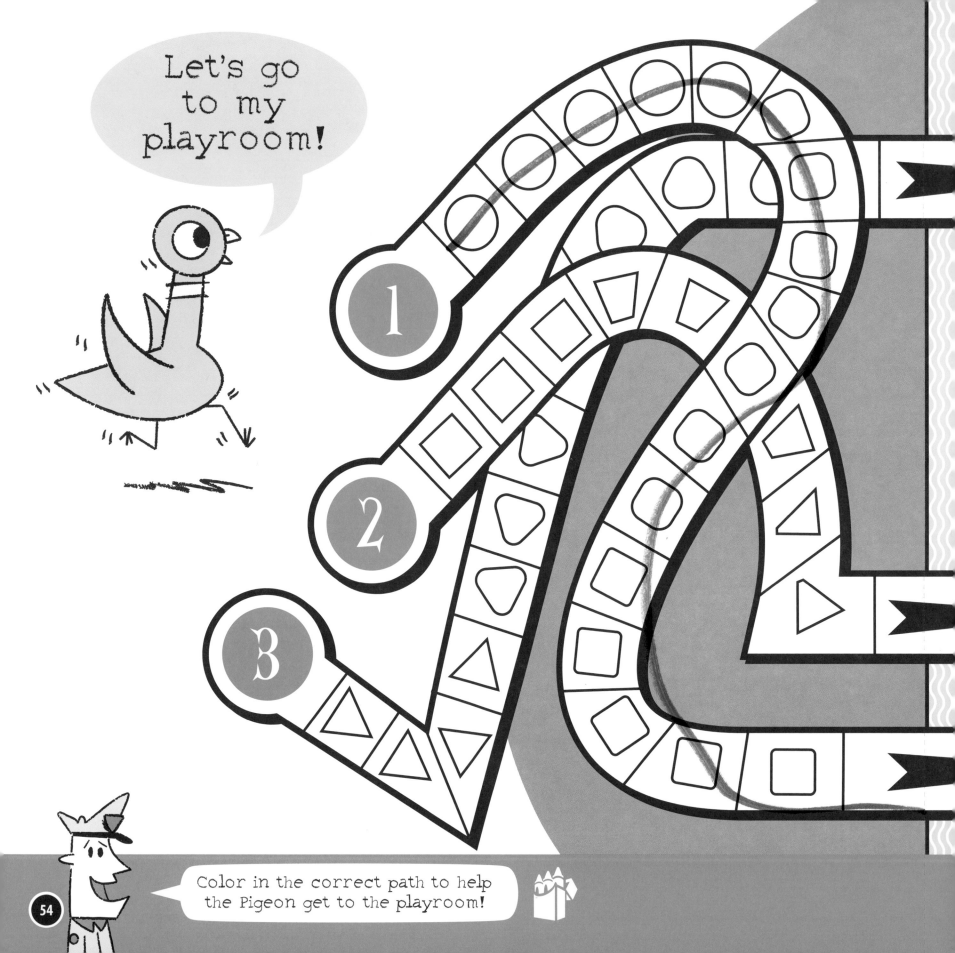

Color the Pigeon's stuff. Then turn the page to finish this activity.

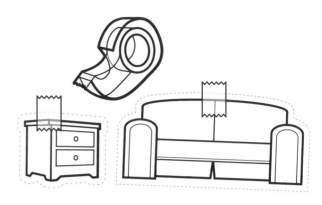

1 Pull out **this page**.

2 Cut out the games and furniture.

3 Tape the pieces in the Pigeon's playroom!

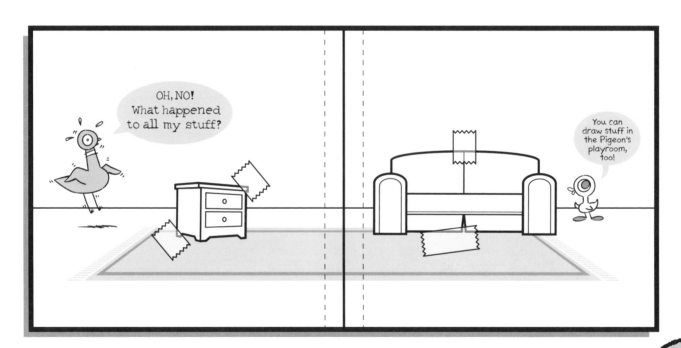

OH, NO! What happened to all my stuff?

You can draw stuff in the Pigeon's playroom, too!

Make my playroom look cool!

 You will need these things to do this activity.

You can draw stuff in the Pigeon's playroom, too!

 Draw yourself sitting in between the Duckling and Pigeon.

Moving all that furniture made me hungry!

Design a crazy rug for the Duckling and Pigeon to stand on! Then, color this page!

The Duckling and Pigeon need a snack!
Draw your favorite foods on this page!

Let's race to the kitchen!

Great idea!

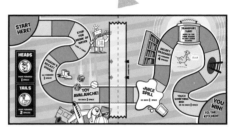

1 Remove **this page** and the **next page**.

2 Lay them flat with the blue side facing up.

3 Tape the pages together where the arrows indicate.

4 You and up to three more players each pick something to use as a game piece. It can be a button, a stamp, a paper clip, or even a torn piece of paper!

5 Place your piece on the game board where it reads "START HERE!"

6 Players take turns flipping the coin. If it's "heads," move forward one space. If it's "tails," move forward two spaces. Then follow the instructions on your square. First player to finish wins!

For this activity, you will need tape, something to use as game pieces, and a coin.

START HERE!

STOP FOR DRINK OF WATER
LOSE A TURN!

HEADS

MOVE FORWARD **1** SPACE!

TAILS

MOVE FORWARD **2** SPACES!

PIGEON'S ROCKET SHOES!
GO FORWARD **1** SPACE!

TOY AVALANCHE!
GO BACK **1** SPACE

CONNECT HERE

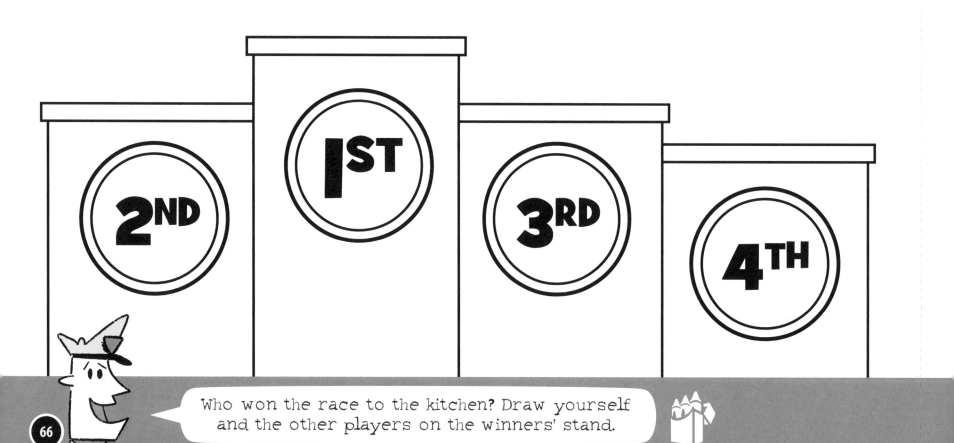

Who won the race to the kitchen? Draw yourself and the other players on the winners' stand.

O B
U C

THE
PIGEON
WANTS
A
SNACK

QUICK! Make up a password and put it on the fridge!

Y

You can also make silly words, like "PANTSY."

EMILY

WRITE YOUR OWN LETTERS IN THE BLANK BOXES ABOVE.

Color the letters, cut them out, and then tape them to the Pigeon's refrigerator to spell funny things!

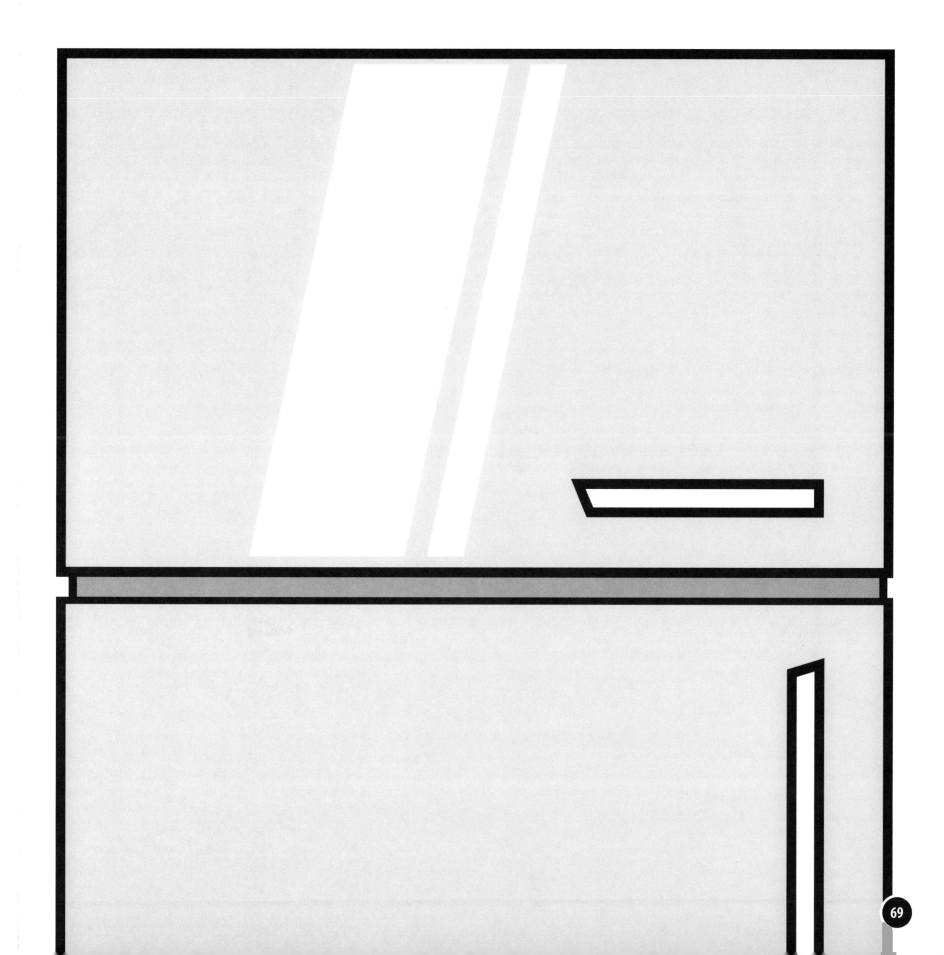

 Draw all types of food in the Pigeon's fridge!

The Pigeon ate so much, he's seeing spots! Fill the page with spots of different colors and sizes!

 The Pigeon sure is excited! Draw lightning all around him, and then color this page!

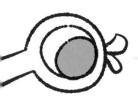

It's time for another
BIG ACTIVITY!
Let's make a picture book!

Hooray!
I'll be a
star!

1 Tear out the **next six pages** of the book.

2 Follow the directions on each page by filling in the blanks and adding illustrations.

3 Once you're done, stack the pages. Make sure they're in the right order!

4 Staple twice at the edge where indicated.

You'll need these things for this activity.
And if you need help, ask a grown-up!

Let's Let the Pigeon

Go to the Fair !

Finally!

words and pictures by Emily Rubbefi

Hi, my name is

___Emily___.

I'm going to leave for a little while. Can you make sure to let the Pigeon

___Go to the___
___Bath room___?

DRAW YOURSELF HERE.

Hi! Can I _Pleas have some_ _Popcorn APPlesause and corn?_

DRAW WHAT YOU'LL LET THE PIGEON DO HERE.

DRAW THE PIGEON'S LEGS DANCING. THE MORE LEGS YOU DRAW THE BETTER!

DRAW YOURSELF SITTING AT THE TABLE. (DON'T FORGET TO DRAW YOUR LUNCH!)

Phew! I think I'll take a break and have a cup of _Arnold Palmer_ before I _have some more cake_ and go on the _swing_ again.

HEY! Come back with my Arnold Palmer you crazy Cow !

DRAW THE MAD COW HOLDING WHAT HE TOOK FROM THE PIGEON.

Oh, no! Mad Cow took away my _Arnold Palmer_, and now I can't _drink_!

DRAW PUFFS OF SMOKE HERE.

DRAW YOURSELF HERE.

The author is
_____7_____ years old
and likes books
about
Wild life
cutestuff corn
style Dolls and Pok
emon

and wants to
Become the
first women
President.

and lives in
Locust Valley
In New
York   !

THE AUTHOR

DRAW YOUR PICTURE IN THE FRAME.

0101100
01011001010110

Published by Pigeon Press
Rat With Wings Blvd.
Coo York, NY oxoxox

STAPLE HERE

STAPLE HERE

Wow! You just finished your very own picture book!

Color the Duckling and then draw confetti all around her!

BESTEST BEST AUTHOR

Color your medal with all of your favorite colors. Then, cut it out and tape it to your chest. You earned it!

Tear out this page! You'll use these things to make your medal.

If you think I'm a better author, you can use this side of the medal!

2nd BESTEST BEST AUTHOR

This is the back of your medal!

A BOOK SIGNING?
I LOVE BOOK SIGNINGS!!!

I better start practicing my autograph!

Draw hearts all over the page!

Here are some autographs by famous people! Practice writing your name in their style, and then your own!

Walt Disney

Ⲩ Pigeon Ⲩ

Mo!

YOUR NAME ➤ Emily

YOUR NAME ➤ Emily

YOUR NAME ➤ Emily

Once you're done, tear this page out. Turn it over, draw yourself, and then tape it up where everyone can see it!

TODAY ONLY!

FAMOUS AUTHOR
BOOK SIGNING

Come one, come all, to hear me read my newest picture book.
There might be snacks and drinks if it's okay with my parents!
But I'll DEFINITELY be signing autographs!

WHEN

(CIRCLE ONE)

AFTER LUNCH

AFTER SCHOOL

AFTER DINNER

or

WHERE

(CIRCLE ONE)

THE KITCHEN

MY ROOM

THE LIVING ROOM

or

THE AUTHOR

Puzzle Solutions

PAGE 21

PAGES 32–33

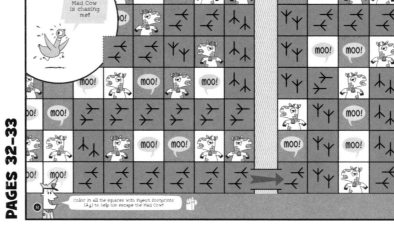

HELP! Mad Cow is chasing me!

Did I lose him?

Color in all the squares with Pigeon footprints to help him escape the Mad Cow!

PAGE 40

What a silly letter!

Scribble out each "BO" to read your letter!

"Would you like to come over to my house for a playdate?

The Pigeon"

Who'dah thunk?

PAGES 42–43

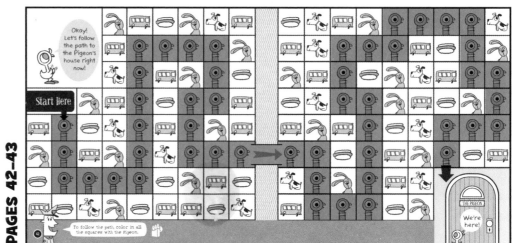

Okay! Let's follow the path to the Pigeon's house right now!

Start Here

We're here!

To follow the path, color in all the squares with the Pigeon.

PAGES 54–55

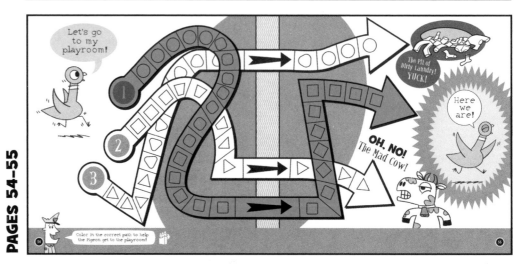

Let's go to my playroom!

The Pit of Dirty Laundry! YUCK!

Here we are!

OH, NO! The Mad Cow!

Color in the correct path to help the Pigeon get to the playroom!